8

兒童
華語課本

CHILDREN'S
CHINESE READER

中英文版

Chinese-English
Edition

OVERSEAS CHINESE AFFAIRS COMMISSION
中華民國僑務委員會印行

序言

　　我國僑胞遍佈全球，為加強服務僑胞，傳揚中華文化，推動華語文教學，本會特邀集華語文學者專家於民國八十二年編製這套「兒童華語課本」教材，並深受各界肯定。近年來，採用本教材之僑校持續增加，為使這套教材更適合海外需求，本會將繼續了解並彙整僑校教師意見，以供未來編修之用。

　　本教材共計十二冊，適於小學一至六年級程度學生使用。每冊四課，以循序漸進的方式編排，不但涵蓋一般問候語到日常生活所需詞彙，並將家庭、學校與人際互動等主題引入課文中。從第七冊起，更加入短文、民俗節慶、寓言及成語故事，使學生在學習華語文的同時，也能對中華文化有所體認。

　　為讓學生充分了解並運用所學語言及文字，編輯小組特別逐冊逐課編寫作業簿，以看圖填字、文句翻譯、問答等方式提供學生多元化練習的機會，進而加強學生的語文能力。

海外華文教材推廣的動力在華文教師，是以在課本、作業簿之外，本套教材另提供教學指引及電化教材，教師可靈活運用其中之各項資料，以加強教學效果，提昇學習興趣。

語言的精進，端賴持續不斷練習，然而海外學習華語文的環境卻有其時間及空間的限制，必須教師、家長與學生三方密切合作，方能克竟其功。我們希望教師能善用本套材之相關教學資源，提供生動活潑的學習環境，學生家長能參與課後各項輔導活動，讓學生在生活化及自然化的情境中學習，以突破學習的困境。

本套教材之編製工作繁複，我們要特別感謝熱心參與的專家學者，由於他們精心地規劃與認真地編寫，使本教材得以順利出版。僑教工作的推展，非一蹴可幾，本會今後將積極結合海內外專家學者及僑教人士，共同為改良華語文教材、提昇華語文教學水準而努力，使僑教工作更為深化扎實。

僑務委員會委員長
張　富　美

FOREWORD

Today overseas compatriots are located in all corners of the world, and it is important that as part of our services to them, we ensure they also have access to the Chinese culture and language education enjoyed by their fellow countrymen. To this end the Overseas Chinese Affairs Commission had invited academics and professionals of Chinese language education to compile the *Children's Chinese Reader* textbook series. Completed in 1993, the compilation received popular acclaim, and since then a continuously increasing number of overseas Chinese schools have based their teaching upon this series. In order to make *Children's Chinese Reader* even better adapted to the needs of overseas teachers and students, the OCAC welcomes the comments and feedback of teachers at overseas Chinese schools for future revisions.

Children's Chinese Reader consists of 12 books and is suitable for primary students from grades 1 to 6. Each book contains 4 step-by-step lessons in increasing levels of difficulty, which not only cover general greetings and vocabulary commonly used in daily life, but also incorporate such themes as family, school and social interactions. Starting from book 7 the lessons introduce short stories, folk celebrations, traditional fables and proverb stories, so that students of the Chinese language may also gain an understanding of Chinese culture.

In order to help students fully comprehend and utilize the vocabulary and knowledge acquired, editors of *Children's Chinese Reader* have designed workbooks that correspond to each textbook in the series. Through fill-in-the-blank questions, sentence translations, and Q and A formats, these workbooks offer students the opportunity to practice in a number of different ways, so as to further enhance their language skills.

Teachers of the Chinese language are the main driving force behind overseas Chinese education. Therefore, in addition to textbooks and workbooks, *Children's Chinese Reader* also offers teaching guidelines and electronic materials that teachers may flexibly adapt as necessary. With these supplementary materials, it is hoped that teachers will be able to inspire the interest of students and achieve their educational goals.

Consistent practice is the key for progress in learning any new language, but students learning the Chinese language overseas are often hampered in their learning environment in terms of time and space. Therefore successful studies will depend on the joint efforts of teachers, parents and students. We hope that teachers will be able to make full use of the educational resources offered by *Children's Chinese Reader* to provide students with a lively and fascinating learning environment. If parents of students can also participate in the various extracurricular activities organized by schools, then students will be able to learn through a daily and natural environment that overcomes barriers to learning.

The compilation of *Children's Chinese Reader* has taken the dedicated and tireless efforts of many people. In particular, we must thank those academics and professionals who have willingly given their time and expertise. It was only because of their meticulous planning and painstaking care in drafting that the series successfully came to be published. Propagation of Chinese language education overseas is not a work that can be completed in the short-term. In the future, the OCAC will continue to cooperate with local and overseas professionals and educators in further improving teaching materials for the Chinese language and enhancing the quality of Chinese language education.

Chang Fu-mei, Ph.D.
Minister of Overseas Chinese Affairs Commission

兒童華語課本中英文版編輯要旨

一、本書為中華民國僑務委員會為配合北美地區華裔子弟適應環境需要而編寫，教材全套共計課本十二冊、作業簿十二冊及教師手冊十二冊。另每課製作六十分鐘錄影帶總計四十八輯，提供教學應用。

二、本書編輯小組及審查委員會於中華民國七十七年十一月正式組成，編輯小組於展開工作前擬定三項原則及五項步驟，期能順利達成教學目標：

　㈠三項原則——

　　⑴介紹中華文化與華人的思維方式，以期海外華裔子弟能了解、欣賞並接納我國文化。

　　⑵教學目標在表達與溝通，以期華裔子弟能聽、說、讀、寫，實際運用中文。

　　⑶教材內容大多取自海外華裔子弟當地日常生活，使其對課文內容產生認同感，增加實際練習機會。

㈡五項步驟——

(1)分析學習者實際需要，進而決定單元內容。

(2)依據兒童心理發展理論擬定課程大綱：由具體事物而逐漸進入抽象、假設和評估階段。

(3)決定字彙、詞彙和句型數量，合理地平均分配於每一單元。

(4)按照上述分析與組織著手寫作課文。

(5)增加照片、插圖、遊戲和活動，期能吸引學童注意力，在愉快的氣氛下有效率地學習。

三、本書第一至三冊俱採注音符號（ㄅ、ㄆ、ㄇ、ㄈ……）及羅馬拼音。第四冊起完全以注音符號與漢字對照為主。

四、本書適用對象包括以下三類學童：

㈠自第一冊開始——在北美洲土生土長、無任何華語基礎與能力者。

㈡自第二冊開始——因家庭影響，能聽說華語，卻不

識漢字者。

(三)自第五或第六冊開始──自國內移民至北美洲，稍具國內基本國語文教育素養；或曾於海外華文學校短期就讀，但識漢字不滿三百字者。

五、本書於初級華語階段，完全以注音符號第一式及第二式介紹日常對話及句型練習，進入第三冊後，乃以海外常用字作有計劃而漸進之逐字介紹，取消注音符號第二式，並反覆練習。全書十二冊共介紹漢字 1160 個，字彙、詞彙共 1536 個，句型 217 個，足供海外華裔子弟閱讀一般書信、報紙及書寫表達之用。並在第十一冊、十二冊增編華人四大節日及風俗習慣作閱讀的練習與參考。

六、本書教學方式採溝通式教學法，著重於日常生活中的表達與溝通和師生間之互動練習。因此第一至七冊完全以對話形態出現；第八冊開始有「自我介紹」、「日記」、「書信」和「故事」等單元，以學生個人

生活經驗為題材，極為實用。

七、本書每一主題深淺度也配合著兒童心理之發展，初級課程以具象實物為主，依語文程度和認知心理之發展逐漸添加抽象思考之概念，以提升學生自然掌握華語文實用能力。初級課程之生字與對話是以口語化的發音為原則，有些字需唸輕聲，語調才能自然。

八、本書編輯旨義，乃在訓練異鄉成長的中華兒女，多少能接受我中華文化之薰陶，毋忘根本，對祖國語言文化維繫著一份血濃於水的情感。

九、本書含教科書、作業簿及教師手冊之編輯小組成員為何景賢博士，宋靜如女士，及王孫元平女士，又經美國及加拿大地區僑校教師多人及夏威夷大學賀上賢教授參與提供意見，李芊小姐、文惠萍小姐校對，始克完成。初版如有疏漏之處，尚祈教師與學生家長不吝惠正。

注音符號第一、二式與通用、漢語拼音對照表

注音符號第一式		注音符號第二式	通用拼音	漢語拼音
（一）聲 母				
唇 音	ㄅㄆㄇㄈ	b p m f	b p m f	b p m f
舌尖音	ㄉㄊㄋㄌ	d t n l	d t n l	d t n l
舌根音	ㄍㄎㄏ	g k h	g k h	g k h
舌面音	ㄐㄑㄒ	j(i) ch(i) sh(i)	ji ci si	j(i) q(i) x(i)
翹舌音	ㄓㄔㄕㄖ	j(r) ch(r) sh r	jh ch sh r	zh ch sh r
舌齒音	ㄗㄘㄙ	tz ts(z) s(z)	z c s	z c s
（二）韻 母				
單 韻	ㄧㄨㄩ	(y) i , u,w iu,yu	(y) i , wu,u yu	i u ü
單 韻	ㄚㄛㄜㄝ	a o e e	a o e ê	a o e ê
複 韻	ㄞㄟㄠㄡ	ai ei au ou	ai ei ao ou	ai ei ao ou
隨聲韻	ㄢㄣㄤㄥ	an en ang eng	an en ang eng	an en ang eng
捲舌韻	ㄦ	er	er	er

目錄
Contents

第一課
Dì Yī Kè

維中
Wei-jung

I 課 文

(Text)

我是男生，我的名子叫維中。今年十歲，但是我長得又高又壯，看起來很像十二歲的孩子。我讀小學五年級，每天早上搭校車去上學。

我們學校在一所教堂的旁邊。學校裡差不多有一百位小朋友。大部分的學生是

白人，有些小朋友是黑人和東方人。我們班上有六個華人小朋友是從台灣來的。

我們是一九八三年來美國的。現在住在紐約。紐約是個很大，很熱鬧的城市。大部分的人很忙碌，但是我們小孩子並不太忙碌。禮拜六，禮拜天我們不必上學，

I 課　文

（Text）

所以我和弟弟妹妹常常跟朋友去打球，有時去打籃球，有時去打乒乓球，也有的時候去打棒球。

每天晚上，我和弟弟妹妹都要做功課。我們一有不會的問題，爸爸媽媽就教我們。有的時候我們討厭做功

課，只想玩電腦。爸媽總

是說做完了功課才可以玩電

腦。我的生活過得很愉快。

Ⅱ 生字生詞

(Vocabulary & Expressions)

1. 男生 boy

2. 維中 a person's given name

3. 壯 well-built, strong

4. 小學 primary school, elementary school

5. 年級 grade

6. 搭 to take (a bus, train, taxi, etc.)

7. 學校 school

8. 所 (measure word for building)

9. 教堂 church

10. 差不多 almost

11. 百 hundred

12. 大部分 most

13. 白人 white people

14. 黑人 black people

15. 東方人 oriental people

16. 班 class

17. 紐約 New York

18. 熱鬧的 bustling

19. 城市	city
20. 忙碌	busy
21. 並	a word used for emphasis
22. 禮拜六 (星期六)	Saturday
23. 禮拜天 (星期天)	Sunday
24. 籃球	basketball
25. 乒乓球	ping pong
26. 功課	homework
27. 問題	question; problem
28. 總是	always
29. 生活	daily life
30. 愉快	happy

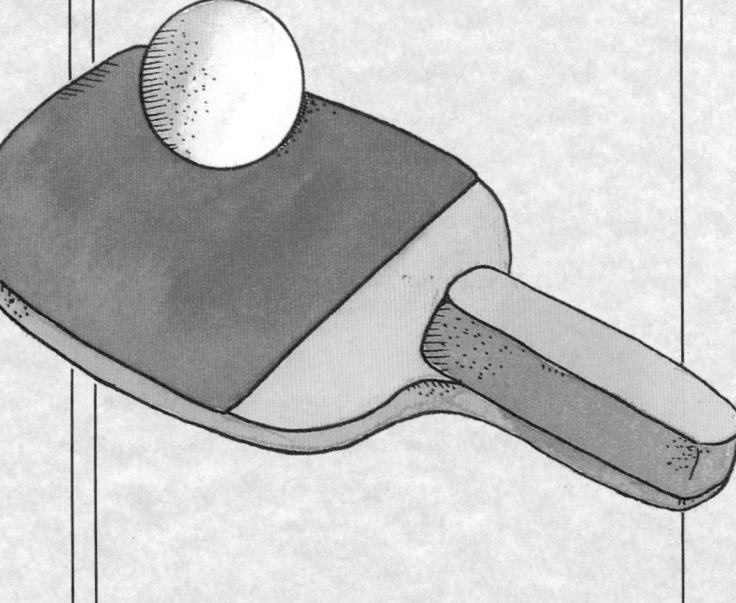

Ⅲ 句型練習

(Pattern Practice)

1. 我　看起來像十二歲的孩子。

   他　　　　十五歲的男生

   猴子　　　九十歲的老公公

2. 他們　是從台灣　來的。

   你們　　　加州

   芬芬　　　台北

3. 我們一有不會的問題，爸媽就教我們。

王芸一生病　爺爺就來看她。

弟弟一高興　我們就要他唱歌。

Ⅳ英 譯

(English Translation)

I'm a boy. My mame is Wei-jung. I'm ten years old this year, but I look like a twelve-year-old because I am both tall and well-built. I'm in fifth grade and I take the school bus to school every morning.

Our school is next to a church. There are a-bout a hundred students in our school. Most of them are white, but some of them are black or oriental. We have six Chinese students from

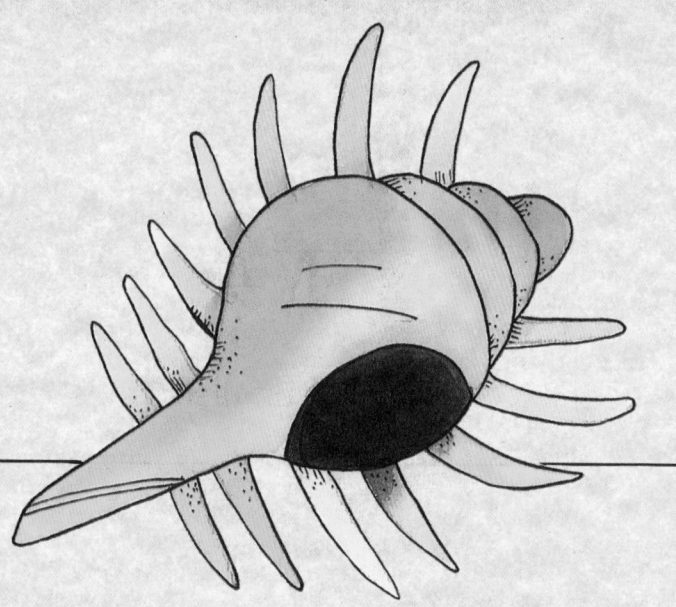

Taiwan in our class.

We came to the United States of America in 1983 and now we live in New York. New York is a large and bustling city. Most people here are very busy, but we children are not. We don't have to go to school on Saturdays and Sundays, so my brother, sister and I often go to play baseball, basketball and ping pong with our friends.

Every evening my brother, sister and I do our

Ⅳ 英 譯

(English Translation)

homework. Whenever we have questions Mom and

Dad help us. Sometimes we hate to do our home-

work, and only feel like playing computer games.

Mom and dad always tell us that we can only play

computer games if we finish our homework. I

enjoy my life very much.

V 寫寫看

Let's learn how to write Chinese characters.
Please follow the stroke order and write each one ten times.

生字及注音	部首	筆　　　　順
只 ㄓˇ	口 ㄎㄡˇ	丨 ㄇ 口 口 只
前 ㄑㄧㄢˊ	刀(刂) ㄉㄠ	丶 丷 䒑 䒑 首 前 前 前 前
成 ㄔㄥˊ	戈 ㄍㄜ	一 厂 万 成 成 成
給 ㄍㄟˇ	糸 ㄇㄧˋ	𠃋 幺 幺 幺 糸 糸 糸 紒 紒 給 給 給
所 ㄙㄨㄛˇ	戶 ㄏㄨˋ	丿 厂 戶 戶 戶 所 所 所（所）
臥 ㄨㄛˋ	臣 ㄔㄣˊ	一 丅 丂 臣 臣 臣 臥 臥（臥）
椅 ㄧˇ	木 ㄇㄨˋ	一 十 才 木 杠 杠 柨 椅 椅 椅 椅 椅
張 ㄓㄤ	弓 ㄍㄨㄥ	一 コ 弓 弓 弜 弡 弡 張 張 張 張
記 ㄐㄧˋ	言 ㄧㄢˊ	丶 亠 亠 亠 亠 言 言 訁 記 記
得 ㄉㄜˊ	彳 ㄔˋ	丿 彡 彳 彳 徂 徂 徂 徥 徥 得 得
地 ㄉㄧˋ	土 ㄊㄨˇ	一 十 土 圠 地 地
毯 ㄊㄢˇ	毛 ㄇㄠˊ	丿 二 三 毛 毛 毛 毯 毯 毯 毯 毯 毯
窗 ㄔㄨㄤ	穴 ㄒㄩㄝˊ	丶 八 宀 穴 穴 穾 窗 窗 窗 窗 窗 窗
放 ㄈㄤˋ	攴(攵) ㄆㄨ	丶 亠 方 方 方 放 放 放
現 ㄒㄧㄢˋ	玉 ㄩˋ	一 二 干 王 玎 玑 玑 珇 珇 現 現
新 ㄒㄧㄣ	斤 ㄐㄧㄣ	丶 亠 亠 立 立 立 辛 辛 亲 亲 新 新 新
鮮 ㄒㄧㄢ	魚 ㄩˊ	丿 ク 勹 各 各 角 角 魚 魚 魚 魚 魚 魚 魚 鮮

V 寫寫看

Let's learn how to write Chinese characters.
Please follow the stroke order and write each one ten times.

生字及注音	部首	筆 順
		鮮鮮
廳 ㄊㄧㄥ	广 ㄧㄢˇ	、一广广广广庐庐庐庐庐庐庐 庐庐庐庐庐庐廳廳廳
檯 ㄊㄞˊ	木 ㄇㄨˋ	一十十才术术产栌栌栌梧 檯檯檯
燈 ㄉㄥ	火 ㄏㄨㄛˇ	、丷少火灯灯灯灯燃燃燃燈燈燈 燈
沙 ㄕㄚ	水 ㄕㄨㄟˇ	、氵氵汀汐沙沙
汽 ㄑㄧˋ	水 ㄕㄨㄟˇ	、氵氵汽汽汽汽
酒 ㄐㄧㄡˇ	水 ㄕㄨㄟˇ	、氵氵汀沂沔酒酒酒酒
書 ㄕㄨ	曰 ㄩㄝ	一一一尹尹尹書書書書
瓷 ㄘˊ	瓦 ㄨㄚˇ	、一二次次次姿姿瓷瓷
器 ㄑㄧˋ	口 ㄎㄡˇ	、口口口叩叩哭哭哭哭器器器
音 ㄧㄣ	音 ㄧㄣ	、一十立立音音音音
響 ㄒㄧㄤˇ	音 ㄧㄣ	ノ乡乡乡乡乡纟绅绅绅鄉鄉鄉 鄉鄉響響響響
錄 ㄌㄨˋ	金 ㄐㄧㄣ	ノ人今今今全金金釘釤釤釤錄錄

生字及注音	部首	筆　　　　　　　　　　　　　　順
		錄錄
影 ㄧㄥˇ	彡 ㄕㄢ	丨 冂 冃 日 日 旦 早 昌 昌 景 景 景 影 影

Ⅵ 讀讀看

Let's learn how to read Chinese characters.

只	只是。只有
現	現在
成	ㄅㄧㄢˋ 成。做成
給	給 ㄅㄚ ㄅㄧˇ 娃娃換衣服
所	所以
臥	臥房
椅	椅子
張	幾張椅子？
記	記得
得	不記得了。覺得
地	地毯
毯	換地毯
前	以前。前面的院子
窗	窗 ㄉㄧㄢˋ。窗子（窗戶）
放	放在那裡？
鮮	新鮮（Fresh）。鮮奶（Fresh milk）
新	新洋裝。新買的
廳	客廳。飯廳

檯	一個檯燈。美國檯燈
燈	紅燈。電燈
沙	沙發。一套沙發
汽	汽水。汽車
酒	水果酒。外國酒
書	書房。看書
瓷	瓷器。一套瓷器
器	買一套瓷器
音	音響放在客廳裡
響	音響
錄	錄音機
影	錄影機

Ⅶ 你會讀下面的句子嗎？

Can you read the following sentences？

1. 這個週末，媽媽要上街買很多 ㄉㄨㄥ ˙ㄒㄧ 。現在我們家裡只有牙膏、牙刷，別的都用完了。也得買 ㄨㄟˋ 生紙跟毛巾。

2. 姐姐也想買一件新洋裝，因為她記得她的朋友要請她參加生日會，可是她要自己去買，還要買一 ㄊㄧㄠˊ ㄙ巾。

3. 哥哥問爸爸可不可以買一個錄影機跟音響放在客廳裏。

4. 媽媽說客廳要換新窗 ㄌㄧㄢˊ ，現在的窗ㄌㄧㄢˊ是黃色的，不好看，地毯也要換成綠色的。她也要買新沙發。

5. 爸爸說，飯廳和書房的椅子也要換，以前是黑的，現在要換成米色的。書房裏要買一個檯燈給孩子們看書用。

6. 哥哥的臥房裏有一張沙發，一 ㄌㄚ 就ㄅㄧㄢˋ 成床了，很好玩。所以我喜歡在那裏玩。

7. 我們家客廳裡有一個 ㄍㄨㄟˋ 子，裏面放了很多外國酒。弟弟說，我們要喝可樂，喝汽水，吃新鮮水果，不喝酒。

8. 還有一個 ㄍㄨㄟˋ 子，有很多很貴的瓷器放在裏面。爸爸說是 ㄍㄨˇ ㄉㄨㄥˇ ，不可以拿出來玩。

9. 小弟弟要給他的小狗買一個狗屋，他說要紅色的。

10. 他買的狗屋跟王小弟家的很像，很好，可是狗不喜歡，我想他要把那個狗屋改變一下就行了。

21

Ⅰ課 文

（ Text ）

海倫是一個九歲的女孩子。她很瘦，留長髮。她媽媽每天早晨替她梳麻花辮子。同學們都說她的辮子很好看。

九年前她在聖瑪麗醫院出生。那時她很胖。鄰居們都說她是小胖妞。她有一個哥哥和一個妹妹。哥哥讀中

學，妹妹上幼稚園。他們常常在一起玩，可是有的時候也會吵架。

　海倫她們住在奧立崗州的一個小城裡。她家的房子前面有一條河，後面有一座山。每天夜裏，河水靜悄悄的流過她的夢鄉。她好喜歡聽水流的聲音。如果有一天

I 課　文

(Text)

河水不流了，　海倫一定會睡不著覺的。

在家裡，　海倫大部分的時候都說中文。上學的時候，　她說英語。　所以海倫會說兩種語言。　她們班上有些同學會說三種話。　比方說 Lisa，Lisa 會說英語，　法語和西班牙話。　因為她爸爸是西班牙人，她媽媽是法國人。

海倫很喜歡她的家，也很喜歡她的朋友。她希望爸媽不要搬家，永遠住在這個可愛的地方。

Ⅱ 生字生詞

（ Vocabulary & Expressions ）

1. 海倫　a person's name

2. 女孩子　girl

3. 留　to wear（ hair style ）

4. 髮　hair

5. 替　for（ a person ）

6. 梳　to comb, to style hair

7. 麻花辮子　French braid

8. 同學　classmate

9. 聖瑪麗　St. Mary's

10. 醫院　hospital

11. 出生　to be born

12. 那時（候）　at that time

13. 鄰居　neighbor

14. 妞　girl

15. 中學　high school, junior high school

16. 幼稚園　kindergarten

17. 吵架　to argue

18. 奧立崗　Oregon

19. 河 ㄏㄜˊ	river	28. 一定 ㄧˊ ㄉㄧㄥˋ	must
20. 座 ㄗㄨㄛˋ	(measure word)	29. 話 ㄏㄨㄚˋ	language
21. 山 ㄕㄢ	mountain	30. 英語 ㄧㄥ ㄩˇ	English
22. 夜 ㄧㄝˋ	late at night	31. 語言 ㄩˇ ㄧㄢˊ	language
23. 靜悄悄地 ㄐㄧㄥˋ ㄑㄧㄠ ㄑㄧㄠ ㄉㄜ	quietly	32. 法語 ㄈㄚˇ ㄩˇ	French
24. 流過 ㄌㄧㄡˊ ㄍㄨㄛˋ	to flow through	33. 西班牙話 ㄒㄧ ㄅㄢ ㄧㄚˊ ㄏㄨㄚˋ	Spanish
25. 夢鄉 ㄇㄥˋ ㄒㄧㄤ	dream	34. 搬家 ㄅㄢ ㄐㄧㄚ	to move (house)
26. 聽 ㄊㄧㄥ	to hear, to listen to	35. 永遠 ㄩㄥˇ ㄩㄢˇ	forever, for good
27. 聲音 ㄕㄥ ㄧㄣ	sound		

Ⅲ 句型練習

(Pattern Practice)

1. 九年前，她在聖瑪麗醫院出生。

    十　　　我　　台大醫院

    十一　　你　　美國加州

2. 她家的房子前面有一條河，後面有一座山。

    我家　　　　　　有一家醫院，旁邊有一個超級市場

    你家　　　　　　左邊有學校，　右邊

有_{ㄧㄡˇ}教_{ㄐㄧㄠˋ}堂_{ㄊㄤˊ}

3. 如_{ㄖㄨˊ}果_{ㄍㄨㄛˇ}有_{ㄧㄡˇ}一_ㄧ天_{ㄊㄧㄢ}河_{ㄏㄜˊ}水_{ㄕㄨㄟˇ}不_{ㄅㄨˋ}流_{ㄌㄧㄡˊ}了_{ㄌㄜ˙}， 她_{ㄊㄚ}一_ㄧ定_{ㄉㄧㄥ}

會_{ㄏㄨㄟ}睡_{ㄕㄨㄟˋ}不_{ㄅㄨˋ}著_{ㄓㄠˊ}覺_{ㄐㄧㄠˋ}的_{ㄉㄜ˙}。

外_{ㄨㄞˋ}婆_{ㄆㄛˊ}來_{ㄌㄞˊ}了_{ㄌㄜ˙}， 我_{ㄨㄛˇ}們_{ㄇㄣ˙}一_ㄧ定_{ㄉㄧㄥ}

會_{ㄏㄨㄟ}很_{ㄏㄣˇ}高_{ㄍㄠ}興_{ㄒㄧㄥ}的_{ㄉㄜ˙}

下_{ㄒㄧㄚˋ}雪_{ㄒㄩㄝˇ}了_{ㄌㄜ˙}， 他_{ㄊㄚ}一_ㄧ定_{ㄉㄧㄥ}

會_{ㄏㄨㄟ}回_{ㄏㄨㄟˊ}家_{ㄐㄧㄚ}的_{ㄉㄜ˙}

Ⅳ 英　譯

(English Translation)

Helen is a nine—year—old girl. She's thin and has long hair. Her mom makes a French braid for her every morning. All of her classmates say it's beautiful.

Nine years ago, she was born in St. Mary's Hospital. She was very plump at that time. Her neighbors said she was a "little plump girl." She has an elder brother and a younger sister. Her brother goes to high school and her sister goes to

kindergarten. They play together a lot, but some-

times they argue.

Helen and her family live in a small town in

Oregon. There is a river in front of her house, and

a mountain behind it. Every night, the river flows

quietly through her dreams. She loves to listen to

the sound of water. If some day the river stopped

flowing, she wouldn't be able to fall asleep.

Helen speaks Chinese most of the time at home.

Ⅳ英　譯

(English Translation)

She speaks English at school, so she can speak two languages. Some of her classmates are able to speak three languages. Lisa, for example, can speak English, French and Spanish, for her father is Spanish and her mother is French.

Helen likes her home and her friends very much. She hopes they will not move, but stay in this lovely place forever.

Ⅴ 寫寫看

Let's learn how to write Chinese characters.
Please follow the stroke order and write each one ten times.

生字及注音	部首	筆　　　　　　　　　　　順
拉ㄌㄚ	手ㄕㄡˇ	一 十 扌 扩 护 拉 拉
忐ㄒㄧㄣ	心ㄒㄧㄣ	丶 心 心 心
又ㄧㄡˋ	又ㄧㄡˋ	フ 又
變ㄅㄧㄢˋ	言ㄧㄢˊ	丶 亠 亠 言 言 言 言 結 結 結 結 結 結 綜 結 綜 綜 綜 綜 綜 變 變
碼ㄇㄚˇ	石ㄕˊ	一 ブ 丆 石 石 石 码 码 码 码 碼 碼 碼 碼 碼
牆ㄑㄧㄤˊ	片ㄆㄧㄢˋ	丶 丬 丬 爿 扩 扩 扩 扩 肸 牉 牉 牆 牆 牆 牆 牆
壁ㄅㄧˋ	土ㄊㄨˇ	丶 ㇆ 尸 尸 尸 启 启 辟 辟 辟 辟 辟 辟 辟 壁 壁
陪ㄆㄟˊ	阜(阝)ㄈㄨˋ	丨 阝 阝 阝 阽 阹 陪 陪 陪 陪
活ㄏㄨㄛˊ	水(氵)ㄕㄨㄟˇ	丶 丶 氵 氵 浐 汗 汗 活 活
櫃ㄍㄨㄟˋ	木ㄇㄨˋ	十 十 才 木 术 柜 柜 柜 柜 柜 柜 柜 櫃 櫃 櫃 櫃
確ㄑㄩㄝˋ	石ㄕˊ	一 ブ 丆 石 石 石 矿 砂 砕 碓 碓 碓 確 確
牌ㄆㄞˊ	片ㄆㄧㄢˋ	丿 丿 尸 片 片 片 牌 牌 牌 牌 牌 牌
線ㄒㄧㄢˋ	糸ㄇㄧˋ	乽 幺 幺 幺 糸 糸 糸 紗 紗 綧 綧 綧 線 線

V 寫 寫 看

Let's learn how to write Chinese characters.
Please follow the stroke order and write each one ten times.

生字及注音	部首	筆 順
租 ㄗㄨ	禾 ㄏㄜˊ	㇒ ㇐ 千 禾 禾 利 和 和 租 租
廚 ㄔㄨˊ	广 ㄧㄢˇ	㇔ ㇒ 广 广 广 庐 庐 庐 唐 廚 廚 廚 廚 廚 廚
浴 ㄩˋ	水(氵) ㄕㄨㄟˇ	㇔ ㇔ ㇒ ㇒ 氵 浐 浐 沧 浴 浴
室 ㄕˋ	宀 ㄇㄧㄢˊ	㇔ ㇔ 宀 宀 宓 宓 室 室 室
正 ㄓㄥ	止 ㄓˇ	㇐ ㇀ 下 下 正 正
陽 ㄧㄤˊ	阜(阝) ㄈㄨˋ	㇗ 阝 阝 阝 阝 阳 阳 阳 阳 阴 陽 陽 陽
台 ㄊㄞˊ	口 ㄎㄡˇ	㇀ ㄥ ㄥ 台 台 台
把 ㄅㄚˇ	手(扌) ㄕㄡˇ	㇐ ㇀ 扌 扫 扣 扣 把
院 ㄩㄢˋ	阜(阝) ㄈㄨˋ	㇗ 阝 阝 阝 阼 陀 陀 陀 陀 院
共 ㄍㄨㄥˋ	八 ㄅㄚ	㇐ ㇐ 廿 共 共 共
肯 ㄎㄣˇ	肉 ㄖㄡˋ	㇀ ㇀ 止 止 片 肯 肯
跑 ㄆㄠˇ	足 ㄗㄨˊ	㇔ 口 口 甲 足 足 趵 趵 趵 跑 跑
處 ㄔㄨˋ	虍 ㄏㄨ	㇒ ㇀ 𠂆 广 庐 虍 虍 虏 虏 處 處
樓 ㄌㄡˊ	木 ㄇㄨˋ	㇐ ㇒ 木 木 术 术 楼 楼 桦 椑 槐 槐 槐 樓 樓
平 ㄆㄥˊ	干 ㄍㄢ	㇐ ㇀ ㄇ 平 平
住 ㄓㄨˋ	人 ㄖㄣˊ	㇒ 亻 亻 仁 仁 住 住
拼 ㄆㄧㄣ	手 ㄕㄡˇ	㇐ ㇀ 扌 扌 扌 折 拼 拼 拼

Ⅵ 讀讀看

Let's learn how to read Chinese characters.

拉	拉 出 來 。 拉 門
心	點 心
又	又 忙 ， 又 累
變	ㄕㄨˋ ㄧㄝˋ 子 變 黃 了
碼	電 話 號 碼
牆	牆 壁
壁	白 色 的 牆 壁
陪	我 陪 姐 姐 去 找 房 子
活	活 動 房 屋
櫃	櫃 子
確	的 確
牌	牌 子
線	牙 線
租	出 租
廚	廚 房
浴	浴 室
室	大 浴 室
正	正 好 ， 正 在 忙

Ⅵ 讀讀看

Let's learn how to read Chinese characters.

陽	陽台
台	一個小陽台
把	把門拉開
院	小院子
共	一共有幾間
肯	小妹妹不肯洗手
跑	跑來跑去
處	到處跑
樓	樓房。樓上（面）。樓下
平	平房。平地
住	住在那裡，住公寓
拼	雙拼的樓房

Ⅶ 你會讀下面的句子嗎？

1. 王 ㄩㄣˊ 的小妹吃完了點心，她把沙發一拉，就變成了一張床，要在這裏睡覺。

2. 媽媽叫她先去洗臉，刷牙，才能睡覺。她不肯去。

3. 小妹說，我太累了，明天再洗臉，刷牙行不行？明天我要早一點起來，陪姐姐去找房子。我先用牙線，好嗎？

4. 爸爸問姐姐為什麼要找房子？她說有一個從 ㄊㄞˊ ㄨㄢ 来的朋友要在美國住一 ㄋㄧㄢˊ，他們請我幫他們找房子。

5. 媽媽說要買，還是要租？要平房，還是要樓房？一共要幾間？

6.他們家一共有五個人，除了爸爸媽媽，還有兩個男孩子，一個女孩子。所以要三房兩廳，有廚房，浴室和一個小陽台。最好是平房，也要有一個小院子，孩子可以到處跑。

7.媽媽說，今天早上正好她看到牆壁上有一個牌子，上面寫 ·ㄓㄨ ，有一棟雙拼屋出租，你去把電話號碼記下來吧！

8.哥哥騎腳踏車陪姐姐去找那所出租的房子，可是因為太貴，他們的朋友沒有很多錢，他們也不喜歡樓房，所以沒有租。

9.爸爸說，她們可以住活動房屋，活動房

屋沒有樓，放假的時候，可以開出去旅行，的確不錯。

10.她的朋友說，活動房屋櫃子太少，他們人多，不夠用，所以不肯租。

第三課 買東西

Dì Sān Kè
Mǎi Dōng Xī

Going Shopping!

I 課　文

（ Text ）

我媽媽很喜歡買東西。她常常逛百貨公司，偶爾也逛大型的購物中心，因為百貨公司就在城裡，但是購物中心離我家很遠。

我認為用信用卡或個人支票付款很方便。不必帶現金很安全。但是爸爸說用信用卡或個人支票有一個缺點

I課 文

（Text）

，就是你會很容易花太多錢或「跳票」，所以爸爸不喜歡用。他也不喜歡逛街買東西。他喜歡跟朋友去釣魚。

媽媽逛百貨公司的時候，通常會帶我和弟弟、妹妹一起去。我挺喜歡跟媽媽一起逛街的，可是弟弟妹妹不喜歡，他們沒有耐心。所以

以媽媽總是把他們留在電動玩具店裡。

大減價的時候，媽媽多半兒（ㄅㄢㄦ）都會買些漂亮的衣服，因為平時太貴。記得有一次西爾斯購物中心的洋裝打七折，媽媽一下子買了五套洋裝。她很高興，因為折扣省了她不少錢。

I 課　文

（Text）

　　　每次媽媽買完了東西一定會帶我們去吃冰淇淋、點心。點心區有各式各樣，香噴噴的東西。我們小孩子最喜歡吃中國點心，像叉燒包、牛肉丸之類的。

　　　回家的路上，媽媽總是會說：「好累！好累！」希望我快快長大，替媽媽開車（ㄔㄜ）， 她（ㄊㄚ）就（ㄐㄧㄡˋ）不（ㄅㄨˋ）會（ㄏㄨㄟˋ）這（ㄓㄜˋ）麼（˙ㄇㄜ）累（ㄌㄟˋ）了（˙ㄌㄜ）。

Ⅱ 生字生詞

（ Vocabulary & Expressions ）

1. 逛（ㄍㄨㄤˋ）　to stroll along the streets, to go window-shopping

2. 百（ㄅㄞˇ）貨（ㄏㄨㄛˋ）公（ㄍㄨㄥ）司（ㄙ）　department store

3. 偶（ㄡˇ）爾（ㄦˇ）　once in a while, occasionally

4. 大（ㄉㄚˋ）型（ㄒㄧㄥˊ）的（ㄉㄜ）　large

5. 購（ㄍㄡˋ）物（ㄨˋ）中（ㄓㄨㄥ）心（ㄒㄧㄣ）　shopping center, shopping mall

6. 遠（ㄩㄢˇ）　far

7. 認（ㄖㄣˋ）為（ㄨㄟˊ）　to think (something), to be of the opinion that...

8. 信（ㄒㄧㄣˋ）用（ㄩㄥˋ）卡（ㄎㄚˇ）　credit card

9. 支（ㄓ）票（ㄆㄧㄠˋ）　check

10. 付（ㄈㄨˋ）款（ㄎㄨㄢˇ）　to pay

11. 方（ㄈㄤ）便（ㄅㄧㄢˋ）　convenient

12. 現（ㄒㄧㄢˋ）金（ㄐㄧㄣ）　cash

13. 缺（ㄑㄩㄝ）點（ㄉㄧㄢˇ）　disadvantage, weak point

14. 容（ㄖㄨㄥˊ）易（ㄧˋ）(一ˋ)　easy

15. 花（ㄏㄨㄚ）　to spend

16. 跳（ㄊㄧㄠˋ）票（ㄆㄧㄠˋ）　to bounce a check

17. 街（ㄐㄧㄝ）　street

18. 釣魚	to fish	
19. 通常	usually	
20. 挺	quite, very	
21. 耐心	patience	
22. 留	to leave behind	
23. 電動玩具店	video game arcade	
24. 大減價	big sale	
25. 多半兒 (半兒)	mostly	
26. 西爾斯	Sears	

27. 打七折	30% off	
28. 貴	expensive	
29. 一下子	at once	
30. 套	(measure word) set	
31. 折扣	discount	
32. 省	to save	
33. 不少	not a little, quite a bit	
34. 點心區	food area	

II 生字生詞

(Vocabulary & Expressions)

35. 香(ㄒㄧㄤ)噴(ㄆㄣ)噴(ㄆㄣ)的(ㄉㄜ) delicious

36. 像(ㄒㄧㄤ)…之(ㄓ)類(ㄌㄟ)的(ㄉㄜ) like...etc.

37. 叉(ㄔㄚ)燒(ㄕㄠ)包(ㄅㄠ) pork bun

38. 牛(ㄋㄧㄡ)肉(ㄖㄡ)丸(ㄨㄢ) beef ball

39. 路(ㄌㄨ) road, way

Ⅲ 句型練習

(Pattern Practice)

1. 她常常逛百貨公司。

   我偶爾逛購物中心。

   李立週末通常去朋友家。

   王芸週末總是去游泳。

2. 用信用卡很方便。

   吃漢堡很方便。

   搭校車很方便。

3. 她買完了東西，一定會吃點心。

   芬芬吃完了飯，一定會吃水果。

Ⅲ 句型練習

（Pattern Practice）

我ㄨㄛˇ做ㄗㄨㄛˋ完ㄨㄢˊ了ㄌㄜ˙功ㄍㄨㄥ課ㄎㄜˋ，一一定ㄉㄧㄥˋ會ㄏㄨㄟˋ看ㄎㄢˋ電ㄉㄧㄢˋ視ㄕˋ。

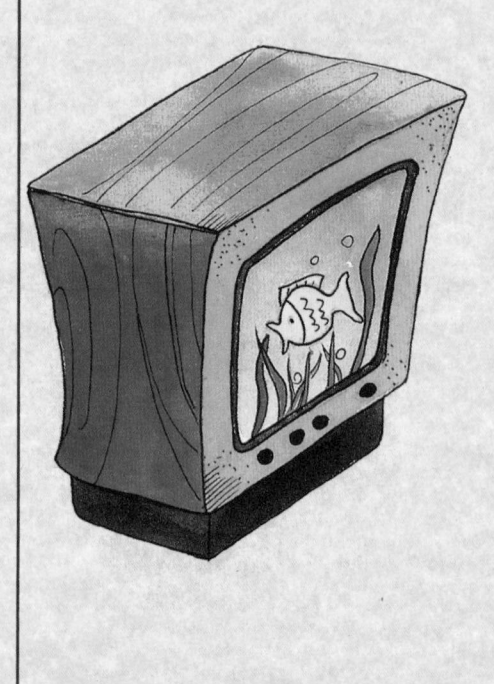

Ⅳ英 譯

(English Translation)

My mom likes to go shopping.　She often goes to department stores, but she goes to the large shopping center only once in a while. This is because the department stores are in town, but the shopping center is far away from our house.

I think paying with credit cards or personal checks is very convenient.　It's very safe not to have to bring cash with you.　But my dad says there is a disadvantage to using credit cards or per-

IV 英 譯

(English Translation)

sonal checks; that is, it's very easy to spend too much money or "bounce a check." Therefore, Dad doesn't like to use them. He doesn't like shopping, either. He likes to go fishing with his friends.

When Mom goes shopping at the department store, she usually brings my younger brother, younger sister and me with her. I really like to go shopping with Mom, but my younger brother and younger sister don't. They don't have any patience. So

Mom always leaves them to play in the video game arcade.

When there's a big sale, Mom most often buys some beautiful clothes, because they are very expensive without a discount. I remember Sears once had a 30% discount on their dresses, and Mom bought five dresses at once. She was very happy, because the discount saved her a lot of money.

Each time Mom finishes her shopping, she takes

IV 英 譯

(English Translation)

us to have some ice cream and snacks. There are all kinds of delicious things in the food area. We children like Chinese snacks best, for example, pork buns, beef balls etc.

On the way home, Mom always says,"I'm tired. I'm tried." I hope I will grow up soon so as to drive for her. Then she won't be so tired.

V 寫寫看

Let's learn how to write Chinese characters.

Please follow the stroke order and write each one ten times.

生字及注音	部首	筆　　　　　　　　順
向 ㄒㄧㄤˋ	口 ㄎㄡˇ	ノ ⺉ 冂 向 向 向
案 ㄢˋ	木 ㄇㄨˋ	ヽ ゛ 宀 宀 安 安 安 宰 案 案
衛 ㄨㄟˋ	行 ㄒㄧㄥˊ	ノ ㇏ ㇒ 彳 彳 彳 衍 衍 衍 徫 徫 徫 衛 衛
寓 ㄩˋ	宀 ㄇㄧㄢˊ	ヽ ゛ 宀 宀 宀 宁 宜 宜 寫 寓 寓 寓
紫 ㄗˇ	糸 ㄇㄧˋ	⼀ ⼁ ⺊ 止 止 此 此 岩 紫 紫 紫 紫
淡 ㄉㄢˋ	水(氵) ㄕㄨㄟˇ	ヽ ゛ 氵 氵 汋 汈 汊 淡 淡 淡 淡
森 ㄙㄣ	木 ㄇㄨˋ	⼀ ⼗ 才 木 木 杏 杏 森 森 森 森 森
林 ㄌㄧㄣˊ	木 ㄇㄨˋ	⼀ ⼗ 才 木 村 村 材 林
希 ㄒㄧ	巾 ㄐㄧㄣ	ノ ㇒ ⺈ 矛 希 希 希
望 ㄨㄤˋ	月 ㄐㄩㄝˋ	ヽ ㇒ 亡 亡 妇 妇 竺 望 望 望 望
派 ㄆㄞˋ	水(氵) ㄕㄨㄟˇ	ヽ ゛ 氵 氵 汇 沪 沠 派 派 派
定 ㄉㄧㄥˋ	宀 ㄇㄧㄢˊ	ヽ ゛ 宀 宀 宁 宇 定 定
絲 ㄙ	糸 ㄇㄧˋ	㇛ ㇛ 幺 幺 幺 糸 紗 絲 絲 絲 絲 絲
算 ㄙㄨㄢˋ	竹 ㄓㄨˊ	ノ ㇒ 竹 竹 竹 竹 笁 笪 笪 算 算 算
術 ㄕㄨˋ	行 ㄒㄧㄥˊ	ノ ㇒ 彳 彳 升 朮 秫 術 術 術 術
預 ㄩˋ	頁 ㄧㄝˋ	㇇ ㇇ ㇇ 予 予 予 預 預 預 預 預 預
報 ㄅㄠˋ	土 ㄊㄨˇ	⼀ ⼗ 土 去 去 去 幸 幸 郣 郣 報

V 寫寫看

Let's learn how to write Chinese characters.
Please follow the stroke order and write each one ten times.

生字及注音	部首	筆　　　　　　　　　　順
溫 ㄨㄣ	水(氵)ㄕㄨㄟ	丶 丶 氵 氵 汩 汩 泀 泀 泀 泀 溫 溫 溫（溫）
低 ㄉㄧ	人(亻)ㄖㄣ	丿 亻 亻 亿 低 低 低
華 ㄏㄨㄚ	艸 ㄘㄠ	丶 十 卄 苁 苎 苎 苎 莲 莲 莲 華
氏 ㄕ	氏 ㄕ	丿 乁 氏 氏
度 ㄉㄨ	广 ㄧㄢ	丶 广 广 庐 庐 庐 庐 度 度
冷 ㄌㄥ	冫ㄅㄧㄥ	丶 冫 冫 冷 冷 冷 冷
戴 ㄉㄞ	戈 ㄍㄜ	一 十 土 吉 吉 吉 吉 吉 查 幸 壹 壹 壹 戴 戴 戴
冬 ㄉㄨㄥ	冫ㄅㄧㄥ	丿 ㄅ 夂 冬 冬
雪 ㄒㄩㄝ	雨 ㄩ	一 厂 戸 冊 雨 雨 雪 雪 雪 雪 雪
高 ㄍㄠ	高 ㄍㄠ	丶 亠 亠 古 古 古 高 高 高 高
山 ㄕㄢ	山 ㄕㄢ	丨 山 山
夏 ㄒㄧㄚ	夊 ㄙㄨㄟ	一 一 丆 丆 百 百 百 戸 夏 夏
春 ㄔㄨㄣ	日 ㄖ	一 二 三 丰 夫 表 春 春 春

Ⅵ 讀 讀 看

Let's learn how to read Chinese characters.

向	方向盤
案	圖案
衛	衛生紙
寓	公寓
紫	紫色
淡	淡紫色
森	森林
林	樹林。森林
希	希望
望	我希望你能來台ㄨㄢ
派	水果派
定	一定
絲	絲巾。絲做的衣服
算	算一算
術	算術
預	預報
報	天氣預報
溫	氣溫

Ⅵ 讀讀看

Let's learn how to read Chinese characters.

低	氣溫太低。山很低
華	華氏。中華（China）。華人（Chinese）
氏	華氏溫度
度	台ㄨㄢ 不用華氏溫度表
冷	天氣太冷
戴	戴手套
冬	冬天
雪	下雪
高	高樓
山	高山
夏	夏天太 ㄖㄜˋ
春	春天溫和

Ⅶ 你會讀下面的句子嗎？

Can you read the following sentences?

1. 弟弟畫的車子有輪子，可是沒有方向盤，怎麼能開 ·ㄋㄜ ？他說，這是圖案，沒有關係。

2. 那種衛生紙是淡紫色的，真好看。姐姐化妝的時候用，因為她喜歡紫色，她也有紫色的絲巾。

3. 氣象預報說，今天氣溫很低，大約是華氏三十一度。出去要穿上毛衣戴上手套，外面一定很冷。

4. 弟弟說，我還是在屋子裡做算術玩電腦吧！院子裡太冷一定不好玩。

5. 台 ㄨㄢ 的天氣很 ㄋㄨㄢˇ 和，冬天城裡不下雪，只有在高山上才看得見雪，所以你不能玩雪。

6. 夏天那裡太 ㄖㄜˋ，我想春天最好，春天台 ㄨㄢ 的氣溫比美國的高。也有很多水果可以吃，可是我最喜歡吃水果派。

7. 我希望住在公寓的頂樓，可以看 ㄩㄢˇ 處綠綠的森林。天空像藍藍的 ㄅㄠˇ 石。天上也有好多星星 (star)，好像很多小眼睛都看著我，跟我說話。

8. 我在公寓頂樓可以看見下面的車子，那麼小，好像我的玩具。可是不是我的 ㄧㄠˊ ㄎㄨㄥˋ 汽車，那些車都開得很快，都不 ㄊㄧㄥˊ。

9.我媽媽希望住在美國的加 ㄓㄡ ，因為
她不喜歡下 ㄩˇ，加 ㄓㄡ 全 ㄋㄧㄢˊ 很
少下 ㄩˇ，也不冷。

10.我覺得秋天去旅行，去森林公園比海洋
公園好，但是哥哥喜歡去海邊，因為他
愛游泳。

體_{ㄊㄧˇ} 育_{ㄩˋ} 課_{ㄎㄜˋ}

P. E. Class

62

I 課　文

（Text）

我和珍妮都很喜歡上體育課。我們倆共用一個櫃子。櫃子裏面除了球鞋，短褲，香皂和毛巾，我們還放了洗面乳。珍妮和我都很愛漂亮。上完體育課，除了淋浴之外，我們一定要好好兒洗個臉。

上課鐘一響，我們就開

I 課　文

（Text）

始作暖身運動。我們先作仰臥起坐，再作伏地挺身。作完了暖身運動，老師才會說，今天要玩什麼？每當老師說今天要打棒球的時候，我最高興了，因為老師總是會選我當隊長，然後我就可以一個一個（的）挑選好朋友當我的隊員。如果是打

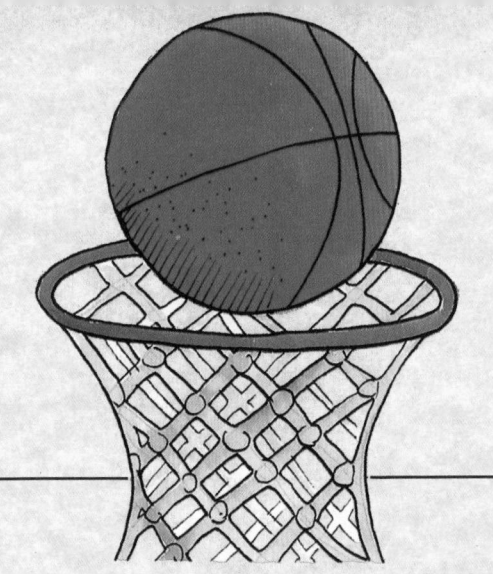

籃球，我就要哭了，因為我是個「矮冬瓜」，矮冬瓜打籃球常會「吃火鍋」。我可不喜歡「火鍋的滋味兒」啊！

打完了球，老師通常會要求我們作點兒柔軟體操，比方說，手碰腳尖。然後大家進更衣室淋浴，換衣服。

I 課 文

（Text）

我們學校的浴室不夠大家同時使用，所以大家得排隊等候。排隊的時候，有些人嘻嘻哈哈，有些人尖聲怪叫。你知道為什麼嗎？只要她們一說到「男生」或「男朋友」就怪叫個沒完。

II 生字生詞

(Vocabulary & Expressions)

1. 體育課 P.E. class, Gym class
2. 珍妮 Janet
3. 倆 two of (us)
4. 共用 to share
5. 球鞋 sneakers, sport shoes
6. 短褲 shorts
7. 香皂 soap
8. 毛巾 towel
9. 洗面乳 face cleansing cream

10. 淋浴 to take a shower
11. 臉 face
12. 鐘 bell
13. 響 to ring
14. 仰臥起坐 sit-ups
15. 伏地挺身 push-ups
16. 每當 whenever, each time
17. 選 to pick
18. 隊長 team captain

II 生字生詞

(Vocabulary & Expressions)

19. 然後	then, thereupon	
18. 隊員	team member	
21. 哭	to cry	
22. 矮冬瓜	short winter melon (short person)	
23. 吃火鍋	literally: to eat hot pot (to have the ball taken away by a taller player, who tries slapping the shorter player's hand)	
24. 滋味(兒)	taste	
25. 要求	to ask, request	

26. 柔軟體操	calisthenics
27. 手碰腳尖	touching your toes
28. 進	to enter
29. 更衣室	the locker room
30. 夠	to be enough
31. 同時	at the same time
32. 使用	to use
33. 排隊	to stand in a queue
34. 等候	to wait

35. 嘻ㄒㄧ 嘻ㄒㄧ 哈ㄏㄚ 哈ㄏㄚ　to tease and laugh

36. 尖ㄐㄧㄢ 聲ㄕㄥ 怪ㄍㄨㄞ 叫ㄐㄧㄠ　to scream

37. 只ㄓㄧˇ 要ㄧㄠˋ　as long as, whenever

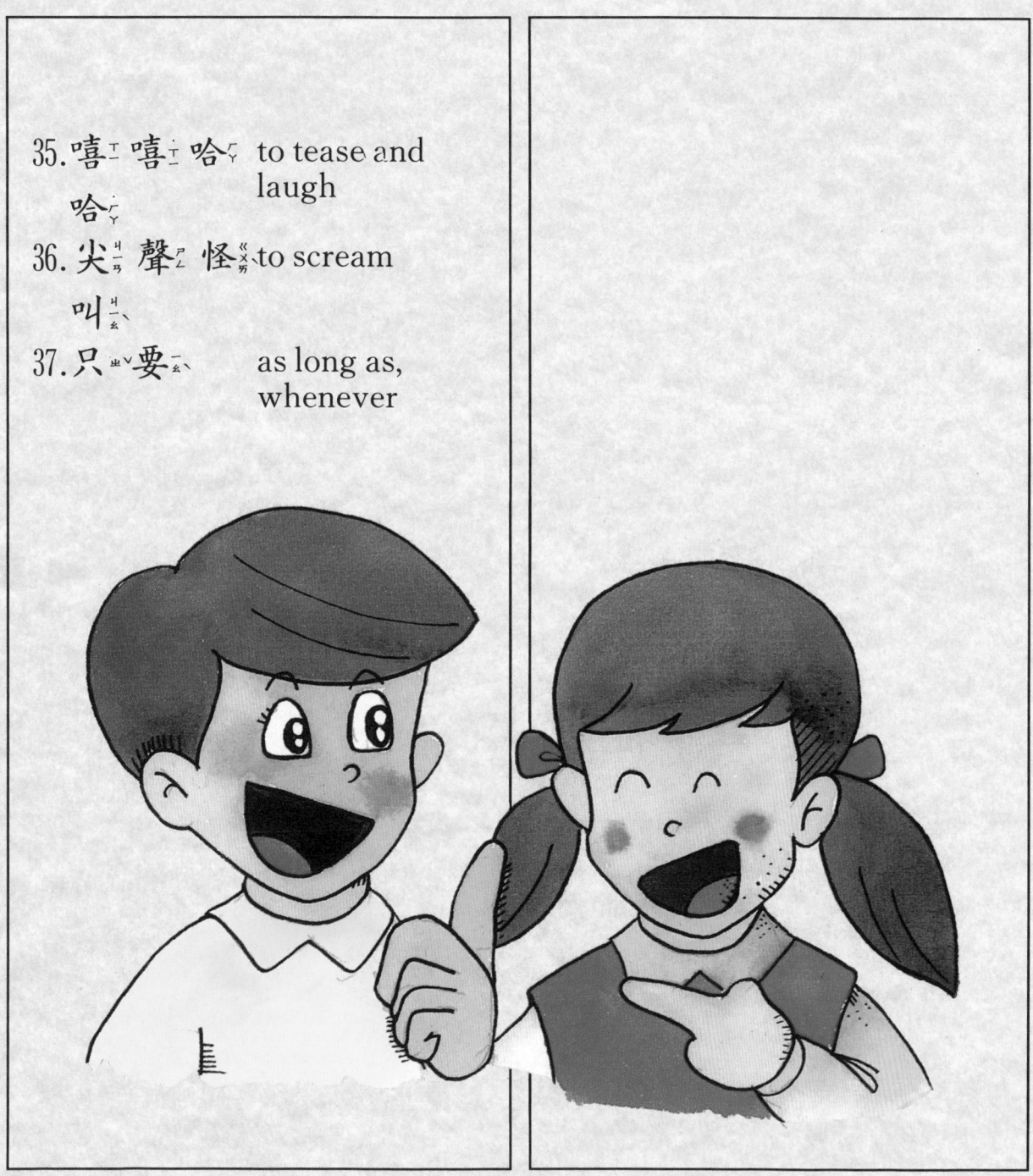

Ⅲ 句型練習

(Pattern Practice)

N 一 V，N 就 Vph 。

1. 鐘　一響，　我們就開始作運動。

　　媽媽一走，　他　就開始哭了。

S 得 Vph 。

2. 大家得排隊等候。

　　我們得認真工作。

　　欣欣得淋浴換衣。

只要 S 一 V 到 N ，就 Vph。

3. 只要她們一說到男生，　就怪叫

個沒完。

只要小弟一看到老虎， 就哭個

沒完。

Ⅳ英 譯

(English Translation)

Both Janet and I like P.E. class. We share a locker. Besides sneakers, shorts, soap and towels, we have some face cleansing cream in the locker. Both Janet and I like grooming. After P.E. class, aside from showering, we always wash our faces very carefully.

As soon as the bell rings, we start our warm-up exercises. We do sit-ups first, then we do push-ups. After warm-up exercises, the teacher will tell

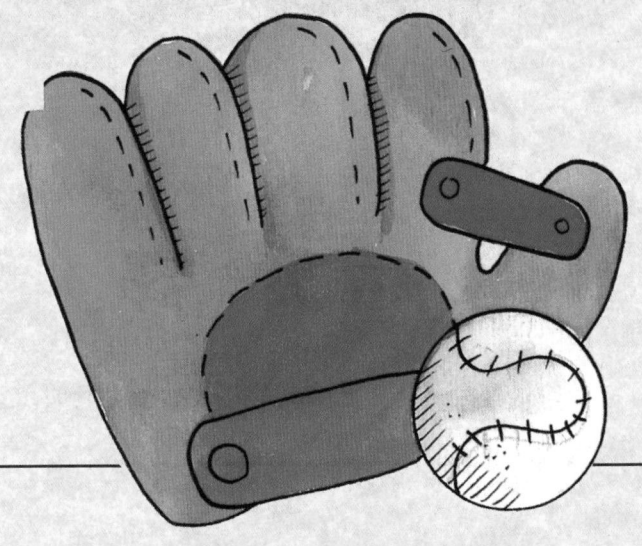

us what the activity is for the day. Whenever our teacher tells us to play baseball, I am very happy, because our teacher always chooses me to be one of the team captains. Then I can pick my good friends one by one to be the members of my team. But if we play basketball, I want to cry, because I am a short winter melon. A short winter melon will often "eat the hot pot." I don't like the taste of the "hot pot."

IV 英 譯

(English Translation)

After the ball game, our teacher will usually ask us to do some calisthenics, such as touching our toes. Then everybody heads back to the locker room, takes showers and changes.

We don't have enough shower rooms for everybody to take a shower at the same time, so we have to queue. While waiting, some tease one another and laugh, others scream. Do you know why they scream? As long as they talk about "boys" or "boyfriends," they scream.

V 寫寫看

Let's learn how to write Chinese characters.

Please follow the stroke order and write each one ten times.

生字及注音	部首	筆　　　　　　　　　　　　　　　　順
秋 ㄑㄧㄡ	禾 ㄏㄜ	ノ 二 千 千 禾 禾 禾 秒 秋
常 ㄔㄤ	巾 ㄐㄧㄣ	丶 丷 当 尚 尚 常 常 常 常 常
樹 ㄕㄨ	木 ㄇㄨ	一 十 才 木 木 杧 杧 桂 桂 桔 桔 桔 桂 桂 樹 樹
葉 ㄧㄝ	艸 ㄘㄠ	丶 丷 丗 荜 荜 荜 葉 葉 葉 葉 葉 葉 葉
每 ㄇㄟ	母 ㄇㄨ	丶 丆 乍 每 每 每 每
年 ㄋㄧㄢ	干 ㄍㄢ	ノ 丶 仁 年 年 年
颱 ㄊㄞ	風 ㄈㄥ	ノ 几 几 凡 凡 凤 凤 風 風 颱 颱 颱 颱 颱
風 ㄈㄥ	風 ㄈㄥ	ノ 几 几 凡 凤 凤 風 風 風
怕 ㄆㄚ	心 ㄒㄧㄣ	丶 忄 忄 忄 忙 怕 怕 怕
晴 ㄑㄧㄥ	日 ㄖ	丨 冂 日 日 日 日 晴 晴 晴 晴 晴
朗 ㄌㄤ	月 ㄩㄝ	丶 ㇇ ㇐ 亨 良 良 良 朗 朗 朗
乾 ㄍㄢ	乙 ㄧ	一 十 古 古 古 直 卓 卓 乾 乾
爽 ㄕㄨㄤ	爻 ㄧㄠ	一 ㇀ 爻 爻 爽 爽 爽 爽 爽 爽 爽
灣 ㄨㄢ	水(氵) ㄕㄨㄟ	丶 丶 氵 氵 氵 氵 氵 泞 泞 泞 灣 灣 灣 灣 灣 灣 灣 灣 灣 灣 灣
乎 ㄏㄨ	ノ ㄆㄝ	丶 丷 ㅛ 쭈 乎

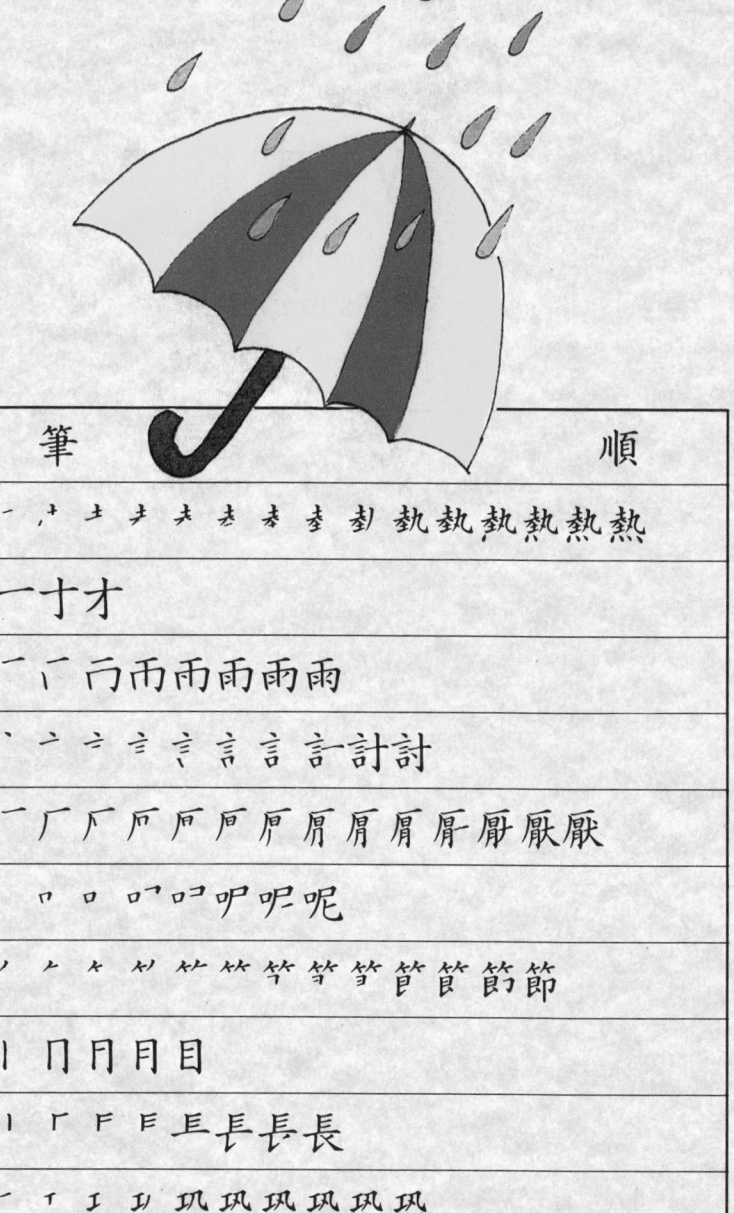

生字及注音	部首	筆　　　　　　　　　　　　順
熱（ㄖㄜˋ）	火（ㄏㄨㄛˇ）	一 十 土 夫 夫 去 夫 幸 刲 刲 刲 刲 熱 熱 熱 熱
才（ㄘㄞˊ）	手（ㄕㄡˇ）	一 十 才
雨（ㄩˇ）	雨（ㄩˇ）	一 ㄇ ㄇ 雨 雨 雨 雨 雨
討（ㄊㄠˇ）	言（一ㄢˊ）	、 二 二 言 言 言 言 討 討
厭（一ㄢ）	厂（ㄏㄢˊ）	一 厂 厂 厅 厅 厭 厭 厭 厭 厭 厭 厭 厭
呢（·ㄋㄜ）	口（ㄎㄡˇ）	、 口 口 口 口 口 呢 呢 呢
節（ㄐㄧㄝˊ）	竹（ㄓㄨˊ）	ノ ケ ケ ケ 竹 竹 竹 竹 笋 竹 竹 節 節
目（ㄇㄨˋ）	目（ㄇㄨˋ）	丨 冂 冃 目 目
長（ㄓㄤˇ）	長（ㄔㄤˊ）	丨 厂 厂 F 乍 長 長 長
恐（ㄎㄨㄥˇ）	心（ㄒㄧㄣ）	一 丁 工 工 巩 巩 巩 恐 恐 恐
龍（ㄌㄨㄥˊ）	龍（ㄌㄨㄥˊ）	、 二 ㄜ 立 立 产 育 育 育 龍 龍 龍 龍 龍 龍
露（ㄌㄨˋ）	雨（ㄩˇ）	一 厂 户 乕 雨 雷 雷 雷 雷 雷 雷 雷 雷 雷 雷 雷 露 露 露 露 露
營（一ㄥˊ）	火（ㄏㄨㄛˇ）	、 、 ⺍ ⺍ ⺍ ⺍ 炒 炒 炒 燃 燃 營 營 營 營 營 營
棟（ㄉㄨㄥˋ）	木（ㄇㄨˋ）	一 十 才 木 杧 杧 杧 柜 柜 棟 棟 棟

V 寫寫看

Let's learn how to write Chinese characters.

Please follow the stroke order and write each one ten times.

生字及注音	部首	筆	順
般ㄅㄢ	舟ㄓㄡ	′ ㇅ 刀 舟 舟 舟 舟 舟 船 般	

VI 讀讀看

Let's learn how to read Chinese characters.

秋	秋天
常	常常。不常
樹	大樹。很高的大樹
葉	樹葉
每	每天
年	每年。每人
颱	颱風
風	大風
怕	可怕。恐怕
晴	晴天
朗	晴朗
乾	太乾
爽	乾爽
灣	台灣
乎	幾乎
熱	夏天很熱。熱起來了
才	高山上才下雪
雨	下雨。雨下得很大

VI 讀 讀 看

Let's learn how to read Chinese characters.

討	討厭
厭	真討厭
呢	為什麼冬天才下雪呢？
節	節目
目	電視節目
長	樹長得很高
恐	恐怕
龍	恐龍
露	露營。露天電影
營	去露營
棟	一棟公寓。這棟樓房
般	一般來說

Ⅶ 你會讀下面的句子嗎？

Can you read the following sentences？

1. 一年裏春、夏、秋、冬，你最喜歡那個時候？

2. 春天，有些地方已經不冷了，有些地方還下雪。台灣的春天不一定，有時候很熱，有時候很冷。

3. 台灣的夏天天氣怎麼樣？跟美國一樣嗎？

4. 夏天很熱，一般來說比美國熱。又常下雨，不乾爽。所以我不喜歡這裏的夏天。

5. 秋天台灣的天氣不錯·ㄅㄚ？你可以去旅行對不對？

VII 你會讀下面的句子嗎？

6. 秋天這裡的樹葉子常常是綠的，不會變黃。也沒有很多紅色、黃色的葉子，可是每年秋天，會有颱風。

7. 你想颱風很可怕嗎？對了，颱風真可怕，風很大，有時候雨也很大，到處都沒有電（electricity）。黑黑的，又不能出去做事，沒有電視節目可以看，只能在屋子裏聊天。

8. 美國的秋天怎麼樣？請你告訴我好嗎？美國很大，每一 ㄓㄡ 的天氣都不太一樣，比方說，加 ㄓㄡ 的秋天晴朗乾爽，全年幾乎不下雨，可以露營，運動。

9. 冬天美國的 Alaska 州最冷，常常下雪，台

灣也冷。可是除了山上下雪，平地不下雪，只下雨，不好玩！

10.有的人喜歡下雪，有的人討厭下雨的天氣，有的人討厭夏天，有的喜歡冬天，人跟人都不一樣，對不對？

11.那棟公寓蓋得真好。冬天 ㄋㄨㄢˇ 和，夏天涼爽。

12.公寓的外面長了很多又高又大的樹，看著真舒服。

13.昨天晚上的電視節目你看了嗎？他們說很早以前恐龍的事情，真有意 ·ㄙ 。

Ⅶ 你 會 讀 下 面 的 句 子 嗎 ？

Can you read the following sentences ?

14. 夏天我們喜歡去海邊玩水，游泳，也可以烤肉，打棒球，我真喜歡夏天。

15. 冬天在 Alaska 州下雪，樹上都是白白的，地上有冰，又很冷。在外面玩要穿很多衣服才不冷，還是秋天跟春天比冬天好玩，你說呢？

注音符號第一式 (WPSI)	生字生詞 Shengtz Shengtsz Vocabulary & Expressions	生字生詞索引 Index 注音符號第二式 (MPSⅡ)	英 譯 English Translation	課次及頁次 Lesson -page
		ㄅ		
ㄅㄞ	白ㄅㄞ人ㄖㄣ	báirén	white people	1-6
	百ㄅㄞ	bǎi	hundred	1-6
	百ㄅㄞ貨ㄏㄨㄛ公ㄍㄨㄥ司ㄙ	bǎihuò gūngsz	department store	3-46
ㄅㄢ	班ㄅㄢ	bān	class	1-6
	搬ㄅㄢ家ㄐㄚ	bānjia	to move (house)	2-27
ㄅㄧㄥ	並ㄅㄧㄥ	bìng	a word used for emphasis	1-7
ㄅㄨ	不ㄅㄨ少ㄕㄠ	bùshǎu	not a little; quite a bit	3-47
		ㄆ		
ㄆㄞ	排ㄆㄞ隊ㄉㄨㄟ	páiduèi	to stand in a queue	4-68
ㄆㄧㄥ	乒ㄆㄧㄥ乓ㄆㄤ球ㄑㄧㄡ	pingpang chióu	ping pong	1-7
		ㄇ		
ㄇㄚ	麻ㄇㄚ花ㄏㄨㄚ辮ㄅㄧㄢ子ㄗ	máhūa biàntz	French braid	2-26
ㄇㄟ	每ㄇㄟ當ㄉㄤ	měidāng	whenever; each time	4-67
ㄇㄠ	毛ㄇㄠ巾ㄐㄧㄣ	máujin	towel	4-67

ㄇㄤ	忙碌ㄌㄨˋ	mánglù	busy	1-7
ㄇㄥ	夢ㄇㄥˋ鄉ㄒㄧㄤ	mèngshiäng	dream	2-27

		ㄈ		

ㄈㄚ	髮ㄈㄚˇ	fǎ	hair	2-26
	法ㄈㄚˋ語ㄩˇ	Fàyǔ	French	2-27
ㄈㄤ	方ㄈㄤ便ㄅㄧㄢˋ	fāngbiàn	convenient	3-46
ㄈㄨ	伏ㄈㄨˊ地ㄉㄧˋ挺ㄊㄧㄥˇ身ㄕㄣ	fúdì tǐngshēn	push-ups	4-67
	付ㄈㄨˋ款ㄎㄨㄢˇ	fù kuǎn	to pay	3-46

		ㄉ		

ㄉㄚ	搭ㄉㄚ	dā	to take (a bus, train, taxi etc...)	1-6
	打ㄉㄚˇ七ㄑㄧ折ㄓㄜˊ	dǎ chī jé	30% off	3-47
	大ㄉㄚˋ部ㄅㄨˋ份ㄈㄣˋ (分ㄈㄣ)	dàbùfen	most	1-6
	大ㄉㄚˋ減ㄐㄧㄢˇ價ㄐㄧㄚˋ	dà jiǎn jià	big sale	3-47
	大ㄉㄚˋ型ㄒㄧㄥˊ的ㄉㄜ	dà shíngde	large	3-46
ㄉㄥ	等ㄉㄥˇ候ㄏㄡˋ	děnghòu	to wait	4-68

生字生詞索引		Index		

注音符號第一式 (WPSI)	生 字 生 詞 Shengtz Shengtsz Vocabulary & Expressions	注音符號第二式 (MPS Ⅱ)	英　　　　　　　譯 English Translation	課次及頁次 Lesson -page
ㄉㄧㄠ	釣魚	diàuyú	to fish	3-47
ㄉㄧㄢ	點心區	diǎnshin chiū	food area	3-47
	電動玩具店	diàndùng wánjiù diàn	video game arcade	3-47
ㄉㄨㄛ	多半兒 (ㄅㄚˋ ㄦ)	duōbàr	mostly	3-47
ㄉㄨㄟ	隊長	duèijǎng	team captain	4-67
	隊員	duèiyuán	team member	4-68
ㄉㄨㄢ	短褲	duǎn kù	shorts	4-67
ㄉㄨㄥ	東方人	dūngfāng reń	oriental people	1-6
ㄊ				
ㄊㄠ	套	tàu	(measure word) set	3-47
ㄊㄧ	體育課	tǐyù kè	P.E. class; Gym class	4-67
	替	tì	for (a person)	2-26
ㄊㄧㄠ	跳票	tiàupiàu	to bounce a check	3-46

ㄊㄧㄥ	聽	tīng	to hear; to listen to	2-27
	挺	tǐng	quite; very	3-47
ㄊㄨㄥ	通常	tūngcháng	usually	3-47
	同學	túngshiué	classmate	2-26
	同時	túng shŕ	at the same time	4-68

<table>
<tr><td colspan="5" align="center">ㄋ</td></tr>
</table>

ㄋㄚ	那時候	nàshŕhòu	at that time	2-26
ㄋㄞ	耐心	nàishin	patience	3-47
ㄋㄢ	男生	nánshēng	boy	1-6
ㄋㄧㄡ	妞	niōu	girl	2-26
	牛肉丸	nióuròu wán	beef ball	3-48
	紐約	Niǒuyuē	New York	1-6
ㄋㄧㄢ	年級	nián jí	grade	1-6
ㄋㄩ	女孩子	niǔ háitz	girl	2-26

<table>
<tr><td colspan="5" align="center">ㄌ</td></tr>
</table>

ㄌㄢ	籃球	lánchióu	basketball	1-7
ㄌㄧㄡ	留	lióu	to wear (hair style)	2-26

注音符號第一式 (WPSI)	生 字 生 詞 Shengtz Shengtsz Vocabulary & Expressions	注音符號第二式 （MPSⅡ）	英　　　　　　　譯 English Translation	課次及頁次 Lesson -page
	留ㄌㄧㄡ	lióu	to leave behind	3-47
	流ㄌㄧㄡ 過ㄍㄨㄛ	lióuguò	to flow through	2-27
ㄌㄧㄢ	臉ㄌㄧㄢ	liǎn	face	4-67
ㄌㄧㄣ	鄰ㄌㄧㄣ 居ㄐㄩ	línjiū	neighbor	2-26
	淋ㄌㄧㄣ 浴ㄩ	línyù	to take a shower	4-67
ㄌㄧㄤ	倆ㄌㄧㄤ	liǎng	two (of us)	4-67
ㄌㄨ	路ㄌㄨ	lù	road; way	3-48
ㄍ				
ㄍㄡ	夠ㄍㄡ	gòu	to be enough	4-68
	購ㄍㄡ 物ㄨ 中ㄓㄨㄥ 心ㄒㄧㄣ	gòuwù jūngshin	shopping center; shopping mall	3-46
ㄍㄥ	更ㄍㄥ 衣ㄧ 室ㄕ	gengyi shr̀	the locker room	4-68
ㄍㄨㄟ	貴ㄍㄨㄟ	guèi	expensive	3-47
ㄍㄨㄤ	逛ㄍㄨㄤ	guàng	to go window-shopping; to stroll along the streets	3-46
ㄍㄨㄥ	功ㄍㄨㄥ 課ㄎㄜ	gungkè	homework	1-7

共用	gùngyùng	to share	4-67

ㄎ				
哭	kū	to cry	4-68

ㄏ				
河	hé	river	2-27
海倫	Hǎilún	(a person's name)	2-26
黑人	heirén	black people	1-6
花	hua	to spend	3-46
話	huà	language	2-27

ㄐ				
街	jie	street	3-46
教堂	jiàutáng	church	1-6
尖聲怪叫	jiānshēng guàijiàu	to scream	4-69
進	jìn	to enter	4-68
靜悄悄地	jìng chiǎuchiǎude	quietly	2-27

ㄑ				
球鞋	chióu shié	sneakers; sport shoes	4-67

注音符號第一式 (WPSI)	生 字 生 詞 Shengtz Shengtsz Vocabulary & Expressions	注音符號第二式 (MPSⅡ)	英　　　　　譯 English Translation	課次及頁次 Lesson -page
ㄑㄩㄝ	缺點	chiuēdiǎn	disadvantage	3-46

<table>
<tr><td colspan="5" align="center">ㄒ</td></tr>
</table>

注音符號第一式	生字生詞	注音符號第二式	英譯	課次及頁次
ㄒㄧ	西班牙話	Shibānyá huà	Spanish	2-27
	嘻嘻哈哈	shishi hāha	to tease and laugh	4-69
	西爾斯	Shiěrsz	Sears	3-47
	洗面乳	shimiàn rǔ	face cleansing cream	4-67
ㄒㄧㄠ	小學	shiǎu shiué	primary school; elementary school	1-6
ㄒㄧㄢ	現金	shiànjin	cash	3-46
ㄒㄧㄣ	信用卡	shinyùng kǎ	credit card	3-46
ㄒㄧㄤ	香噴噴的	shiāngpēnpēnde	delicious	3-48
	香皂	shiāng tzàu	soap	4-67
	響	shiǎng	to ring	4-67
	像……之類的	shiàng...jr lèide	like...etc.	3-48

ㄒ一ㄥ	星ㄒ一ㄥ 期ㄑㄧˊ 天ㄊㄧㄢ	Shīngchí tiān	Sunday	1-7
	星ㄒ一ㄥ 期ㄑㄧˊ 六ㄌㄧㄡˋ	Shīngchí liòu	Saturday	1-7
ㄒㄩㄝˊ	學ㄒㄩㄝˊ 校ㄒ一ㄠˋ	shiuéshiàu	school	1-6
ㄒㄩㄢˇ	選ㄒㄩㄢˇ	shiuǎn	to pick	4-67
ㄓ				
ㄓ	支ㄓ 票ㄆ一ㄠˋ	jrpiàu	check	3-46
	只ㄓˇ 要ㄧㄠˋ	jřyàu	as long as; whenever	4-69
ㄓㄜ	折ㄓㄜˊ 扣ㄎㄡˋ	jé kòu	discount	3-47
ㄓㄣ	珍ㄓㄣ 妮ㄋㄧˊ	Jēnni	Janet	4-67
ㄓㄨㄤ	壯ㄓㄨㄤˋ	juàng	well-built; strong	1-6
ㄓㄨㄥ	鐘ㄓㄨㄥ	jūng	bell	4-67
	中ㄓㄨㄥ 學ㄒㄩㄝˊ	jūngshiué	high school; junior high school	2-26
ㄔ				
ㄔ	吃ㄔ 火ㄏㄨㄛˇ 鍋ㄍㄨㄛ	chr huǒguō	literally: to eat hot pot (to have the ball taken away by a taller player, who tries slapping the shorter player's hand)	4-68

生字生詞索引 Index

注音符號第一式 (WPSI)	生 字 生 詞 Shengtz Shengtsz Vocabulary & Expressions	注音符號第二式 (MPSⅡ)	英　　　　　　　譯 English Translation	課次及頁次 Lesson -page
ㄔㄚ	叉燒包	chāshāu bāu	pork bun	3-48
	差不多	chàbuduō	almost	1-6
ㄔㄠ	吵架	chǎujià	to argue	2-26
ㄔㄥ	城市	chéngshr̀	city	1-7
ㄔㄨ	出生	chūshēng	to be born	2-26
ㄕ				
ㄕ	使用	shǐ yùng	to use	4-68
ㄕㄡ	手碰腳尖	shǒupèng jiǎujiān	touching your toes	4-68
ㄕㄢ	山	shān	mountain	2-27
ㄕㄥ	生活	shēnghuó	daily life	1-7
	聲音	shēngyin	sound	2-27
	省	shěng	to save	3-47
	聖瑪麗	Shèngmǎli	St. Mary's	2-26
ㄕㄨ	梳	shū	to comb; to style hair	2-26
ㄖ				

ㄖㄜ	熱鬧的	rènàude	bustling	1-6
ㄖㄡ	柔軟體操	róuruǎn tǐtsāu	calisthenics	4-68
ㄖㄢ	然後	ránhòu	then; thereupon	4-68
ㄖㄣ	認為	rènwéi	to think (something); to be of the opinion that...	3-46
ㄖㄨㄥ	容易（一）	rúngyi（yì）	easy	3-46

ㄗ

ㄗ	滋味（兒）	tzwèi(r)	taste	4-68
ㄗㄨㄛ	座	tzuò	(measure word) for mountain	2-27
ㄗㄨㄥ	總是	tzǔngshr̀	always	1-7

ㄙ

ㄙㄨㄛ	所	suǒ	(measure word) for building	1-6

ㄞ

ㄞ	矮冬瓜	ǎi dūngguā	short winter melon (short person)	4-68

ㄠ

ㄠ	奧立崗	Àu lì gāng	Oregon	2-26

ㄡ

生字生詞索引		Index		

	語ㄩˇ言ㄧㄢˊ	yǔyán	language	2-27
ㄩㄢ	遠ㄩㄢˇ	yuǎn	far	3-46
ㄩㄥ	永ㄩㄥˇ遠ㄩㄢˇ	yǔngyuǎn	forever; for good	2-27

快樂的小魚

黃昭雄 曲

我家住在綠水中，游來游去樂融融。

綠水茫茫無邊際，住在水中真有趣。

蝦兵蟹將好朋友，隨波逐浪趣味濃。

但願漁翁不來擾，自由自在樂無窮。

秋（くーヌ）夜（ーせ）

恩（ㄣˊ）雨（ㄩˇ） 詞（ㄘˊ）曲（ㄑㄩˇ）

亮（ㄌㄧㄤˋ）晶（ㄐㄧㄥ）晶（ㄐㄧㄥ）， 亮（ㄌㄧㄤˋ）晶（ㄐㄧㄥ）晶（ㄐㄧㄥ）， 天（ㄊㄧㄢ）上（ㄕㄤˋ）閃（ㄕㄢˇ）著（ㄓㄜ） 小（ㄒㄧㄠˇ）星（ㄒㄧㄥ）星（ㄒㄧㄥ），

滿（ㄇㄢˇ）盈（ㄧㄥˊ）盈（ㄧㄥˊ）， 滿（ㄇㄢˇ）盈（ㄧㄥˊ）盈（ㄧㄥˊ）， 一（ㄧ）輪（ㄌㄨㄣˊ）明（ㄇㄧㄥˊ）月（ㄩㄝˋ） 由（ㄧㄡˊ）東（ㄉㄨㄥ）升（ㄕㄥ）。

星（ㄒㄧㄥ） 星（ㄒㄧㄥ）呀 請（ㄑㄧㄥˇ）問（ㄨㄣˋ）你（ㄋㄧˇ）：「你（ㄋㄧˇ）像（ㄒㄧㄤˋ）誰（ㄕㄟˊ）眼（ㄧㄢˇ） 睛（ㄐㄧㄥ）？」

明月呀 請問你：「你像誰面型？」

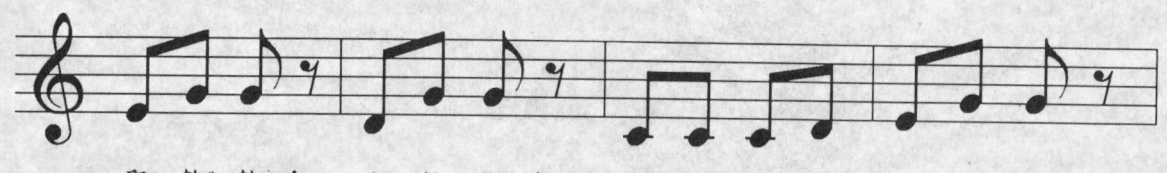

唧鈴鈴！ 唧鈴鈴！ 蟲兒奏樂真好聽，

唧鈴鈴！ 唧鈴鈴！ 好像姊姊在彈琴。

茉莉花

中國民謠
村谷達也編曲

Moderato

满枝桠，又香又白人人夸，

让我来将你摘下，

让我来将你摘下，

兒童華語課本（八）中英文版

主　　　編：王孫元平、何景賢、宋靜如、馬昭華、葉德明

出版機關：中華民國僑務委員會

　　　　　地址：台北市徐州路五號十六樓

　　　　　電話：(02) 2327-2600

　　　　　網址：http://www.ocac.gov.tw

出版年月：中華民國八十二年七月初版

版(刷)次：中華民國九十四年九月初版十刷

定　　　價：新台幣八十元

展 售 處：國家書坊台視總店（台北市八德路三段 10 號，電話：02-25781515）

　　　　　五南文化廣場（台中市中山路 6 號，電話：04-22260330）

承　　　印：仁翔美術印刷股份有限公司

GPN：011099860080

ISBN：957-02-0736-1